First Learning

Early Writing

sheep

SCHOLASTIC

How to use this book

Make the activities in this book a fun part of your child's everyday routine but never spend too long on the activities.

Work through the book together in a logical order, starting at the beginning. The content is broadly divided into two sections as follows:

Patterning: When children are making these early marks, they are learning to hold a pencil and attempting to control their marks with their muscles. This enhances their fine motor skills and helps to develop their hand-eye coordination before actually forming letters.

Shape names: Children move on to forming letters – both lowercase and uppercase. The lowercase letters are grouped into different shapes:

- Straight down letters (l, t, i, u, y, j) that start at the top and are drawn with a line straight down.
- Down, up and over letters (r, n, m, h, p, b, k) that start at the top and are drawn with a line straight down, back up along the same line and then arch over to the right.
- Up, backwards and around letters (c, a, d, g, q, o, s, f, e) that start at 1 o'clock and go up, backwards and around.
- Zooming letters (v, w, x, z) that incorporate straight zig-zagged lines.

Read the instructions on each page together, moving your finger along the words as you read. Encourage your child to join in with familiar words and numbers. Check that your child understands what is required before each activity, for example by explaining words or phrases such as 'curved' or 'slanted'.

Always praise and encourage your child. Find something good to talk about and never respond negatively to their work. Instead, suggest trying again so that you can give a little help.

Lenny Lizard

Lenny Lizard appears on tramlines to support letter formation. His 'head', 'body' and 'tail' act as reminders for letter size

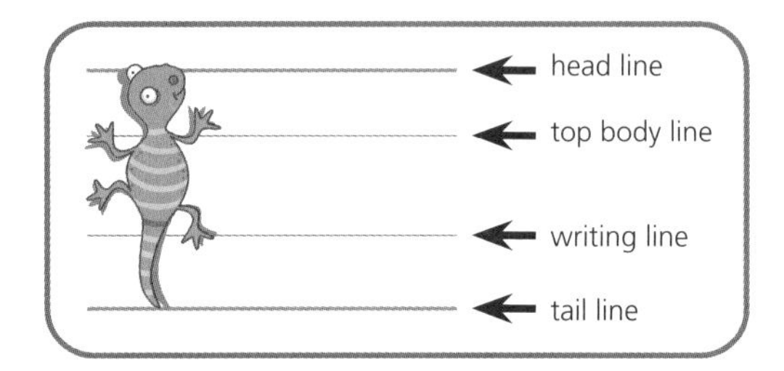

Free letter movies

Play the free animations, showing the formation of each lowercase letter. Visit www.scholastic.co.uk/FLEWW35. You will also find online a copy of the certificate on page 32, as well as a full set of answers. Finally, there is also some useful information about supporting right and left handed children plus some exercises you can do to support your child's writing development.

www.scholastic.co.uk/FLEWW35

Published in the UK by Scholastic Education, 2022

Scholastic Distribution Centre, Bosworth Avenue, Tournament Fields, Warwick, CV34 6UQ

Scholastic Ireland, 89E Lagan Road, Dublin Industrial Estate, Glasnevin, Dublin, D11 HP5F

www.scholastic.co.uk

3 4 5 6 7 8 9   2 3 4 5 6 7 8 9 0 1

A CIP catalogue record for this book is available from the British Library.

ISBN 978-1407-18357-2

This Book was printed by Leo Paper Products Ltd, Heshan Astros Printing Limited, XuanTan Temple Industrial Zone, Gulao Town, Heshan City, Guangdong Province, China.

The book is made of materials from well-managed, FSC®-certified forests and other controlled sources.

Author
Amanda McLeod

Editorial team
Rachel Morgan, Robin Hunt

Design team
Dipa Mistry, Andrew Magee

Illustration
Jim Peacock, pages 16-23 Shutterstock

Contents

First marks

Draw lines, dots and squiggles.

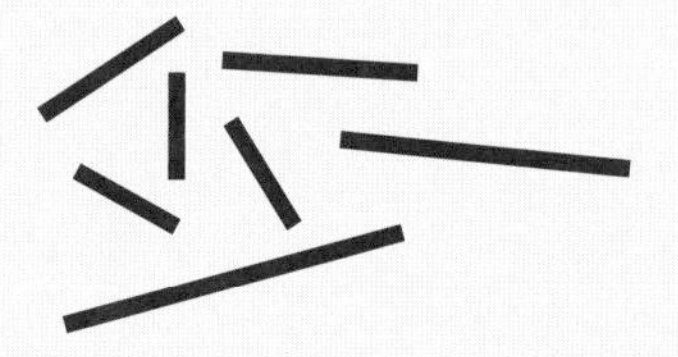

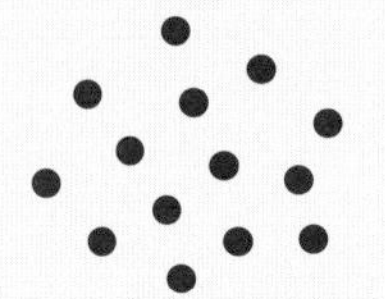

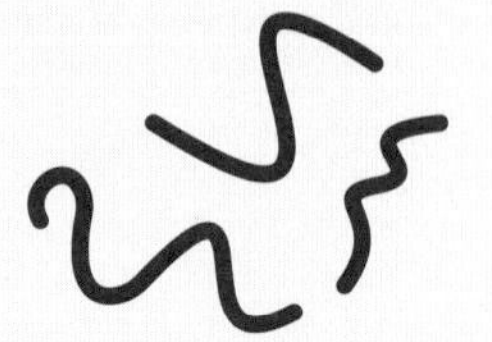

Draw lines

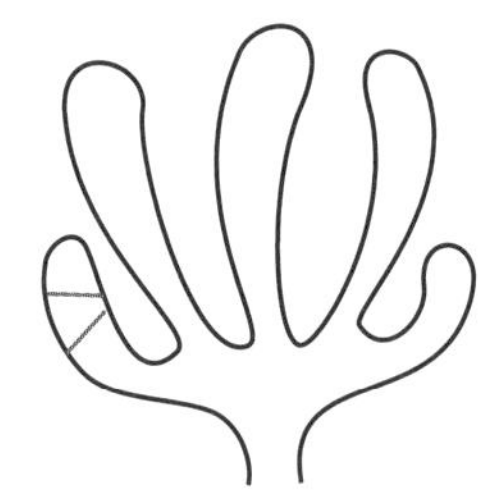

Draw dots

Draw squiggles

First lines

Lines can be straight, curved or wavy. Draw lines to help the dogs reach their balls.

straight **curved** **wavy**

Trace with your fingers before you use your pencil.

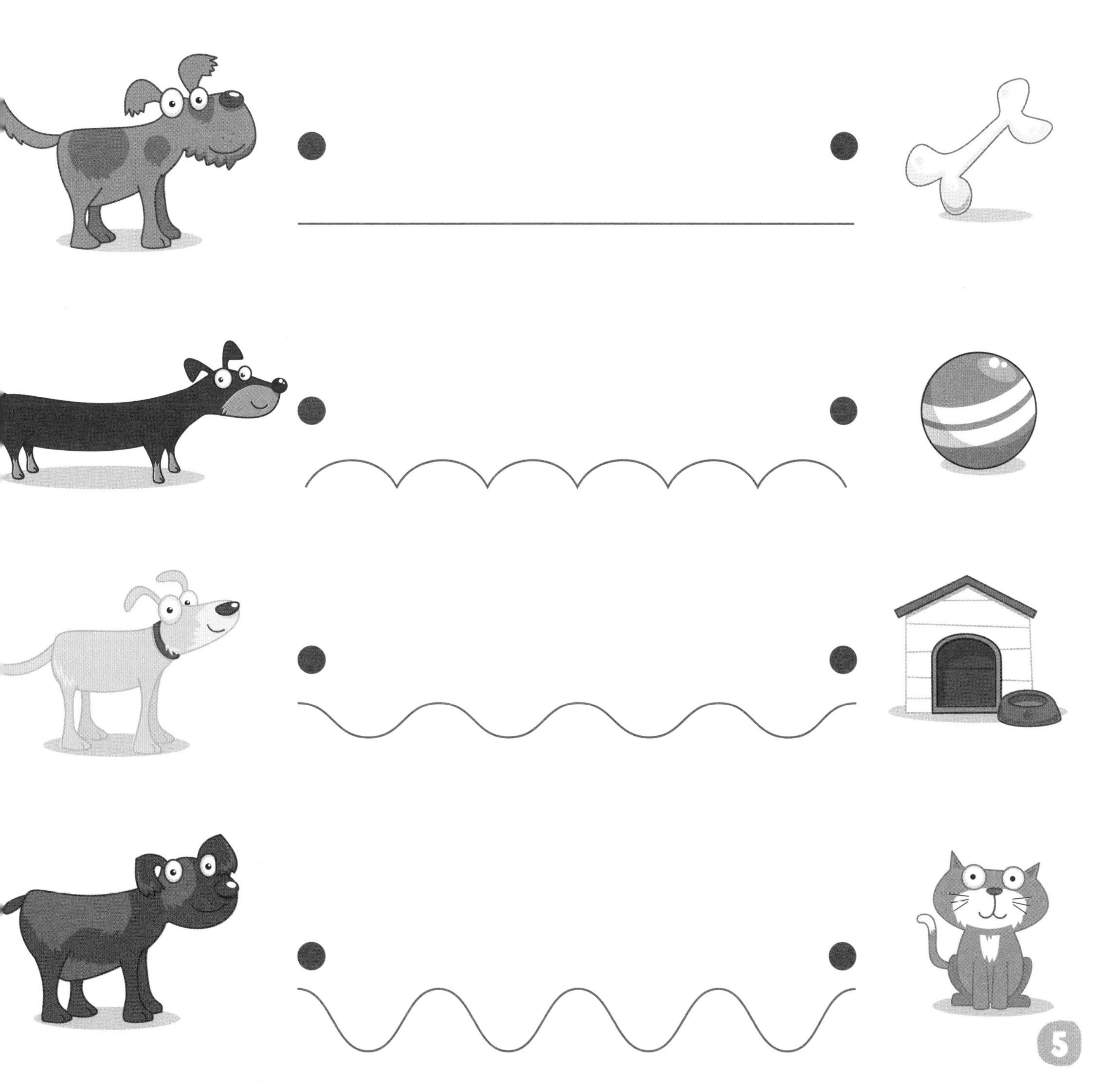

First shape patterns

You can draw some shapes using straight or curved lines.

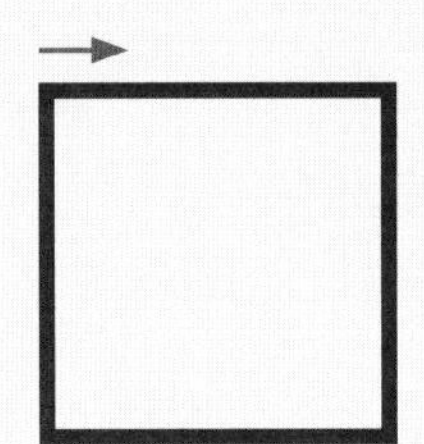

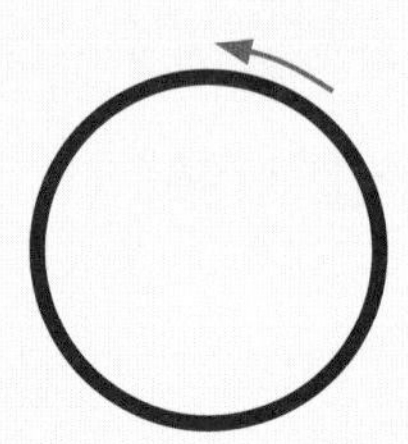

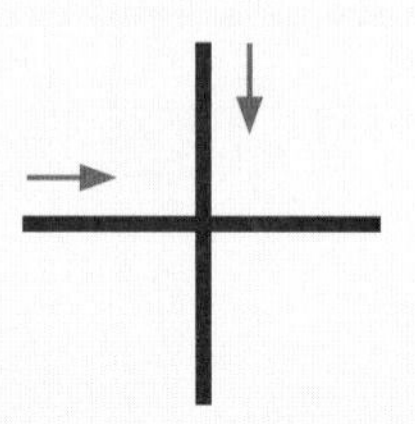

Trace over the shapes. Trace with your fingers before you use your pencil.

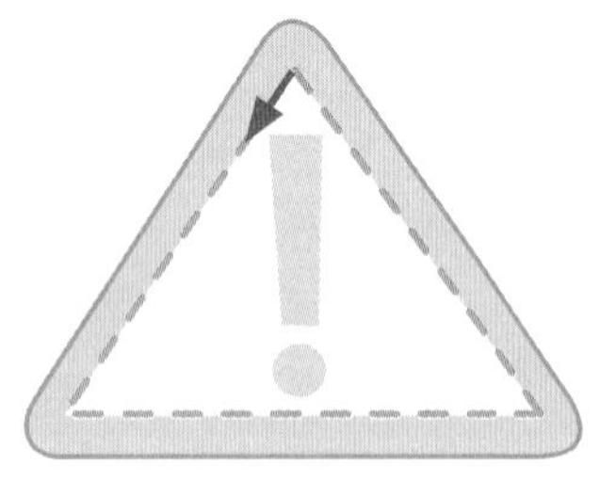

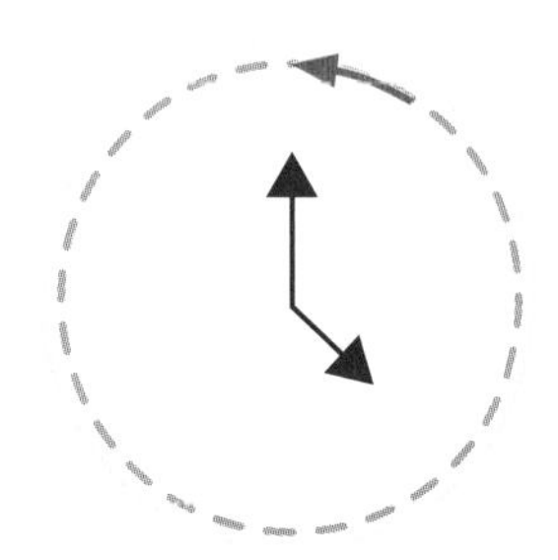

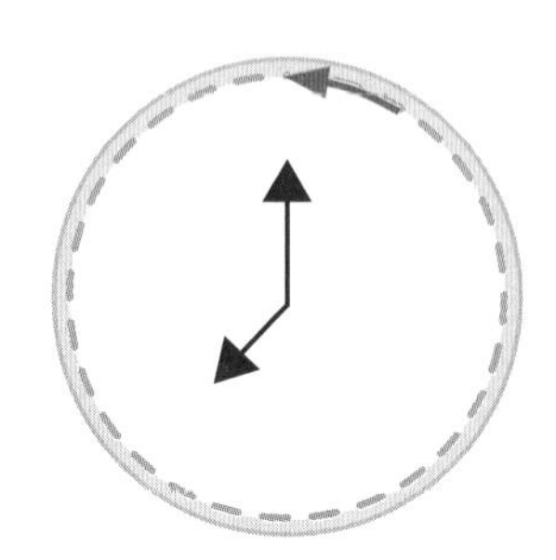

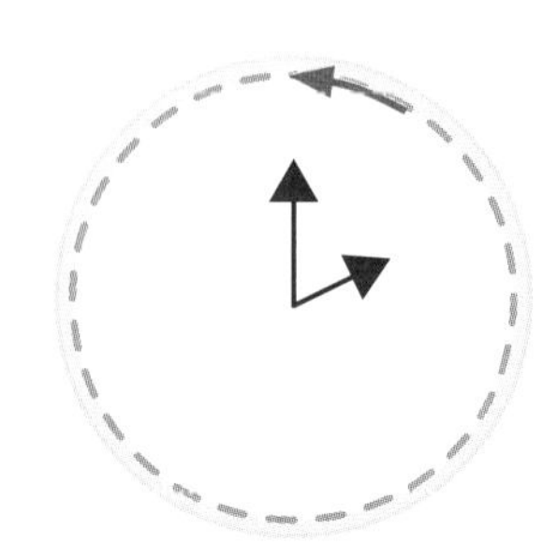

First flow

Continue these patterns to grow the plants.

They include spirals, loops, arches and waves

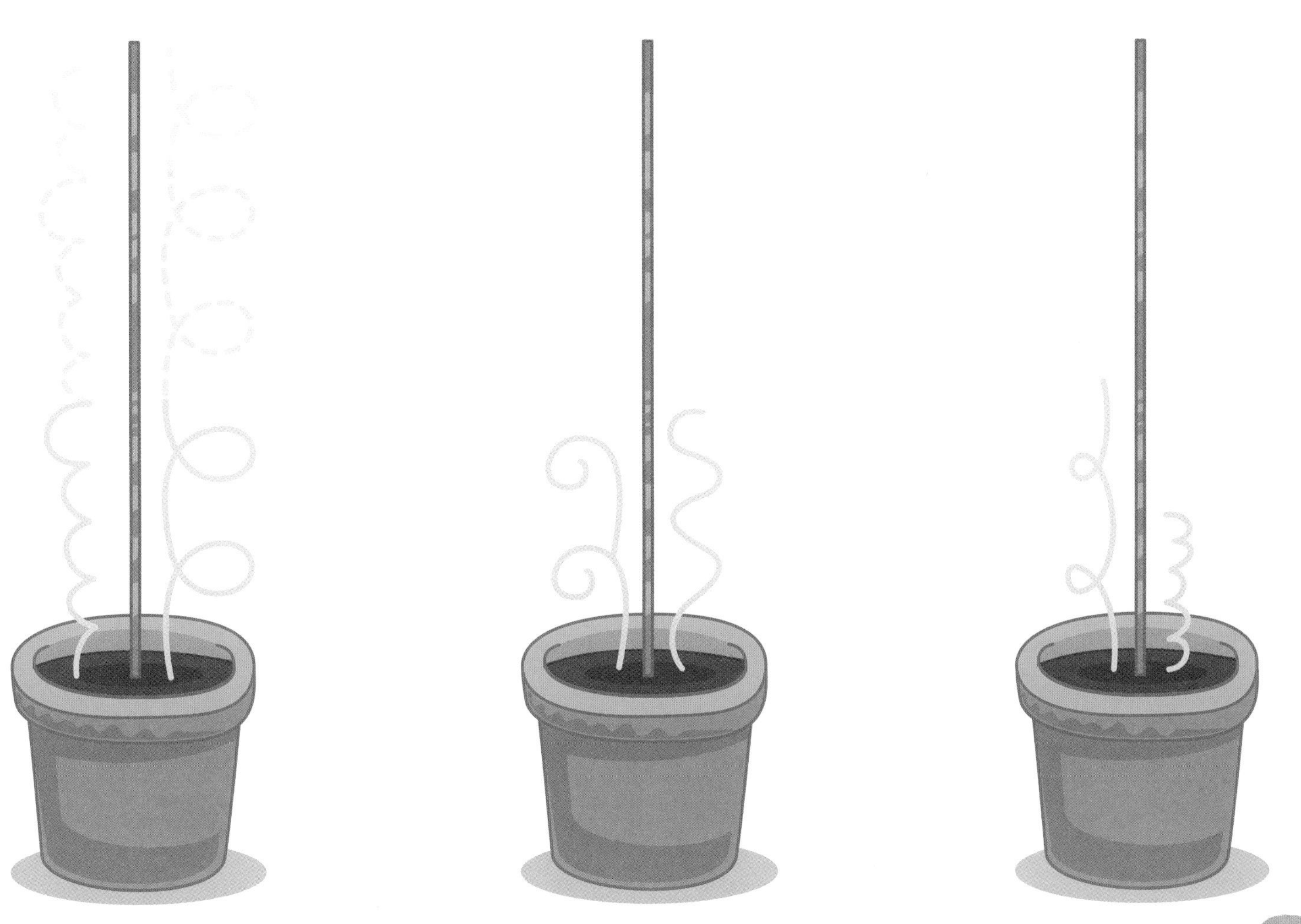

First slants, zigzags and crosses

Slanted lines lean to the side. / / / / / / /

Zigzags are made up of up and down slanted lines.

Crosses can be made up of two slanted lines.

X X X X X X

Trace over the patterns with your pencil.

First patterns picture

Trace the patterns on the genie's carpet with your pencil. Add more patterns to the carpet.

First straight down letter shapes

Start at the top and go straight down.

Trace over the letters and write some of your own.

Notes: These six letters are made using straight lines that start from the top and go down to the writing line first of all. The vertical lines in **u** and **y** must be parallel.

First down, up and over letter shapes

Start at the top and go straight down, freeze, then straight back up and over. Trace and continue this pattern

Practise: trace the patterns you need to write these letters.

Trace over the letter and write some of your own.

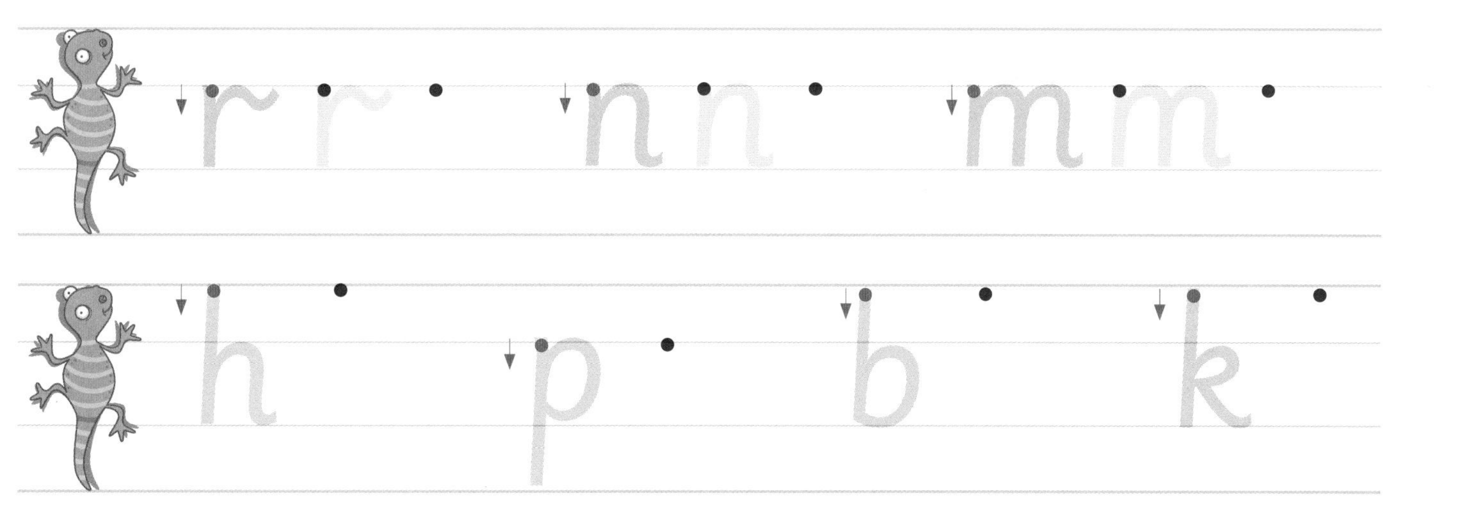

Notes: These seven letters are made using straight lines and curves. Remember to exit your **r** back up at the top.

First up, back and around letter shapes

Trace over the curves.

Put the wool on the sheep and the leaves on the tree.

Trace over the letters and write some of your own.

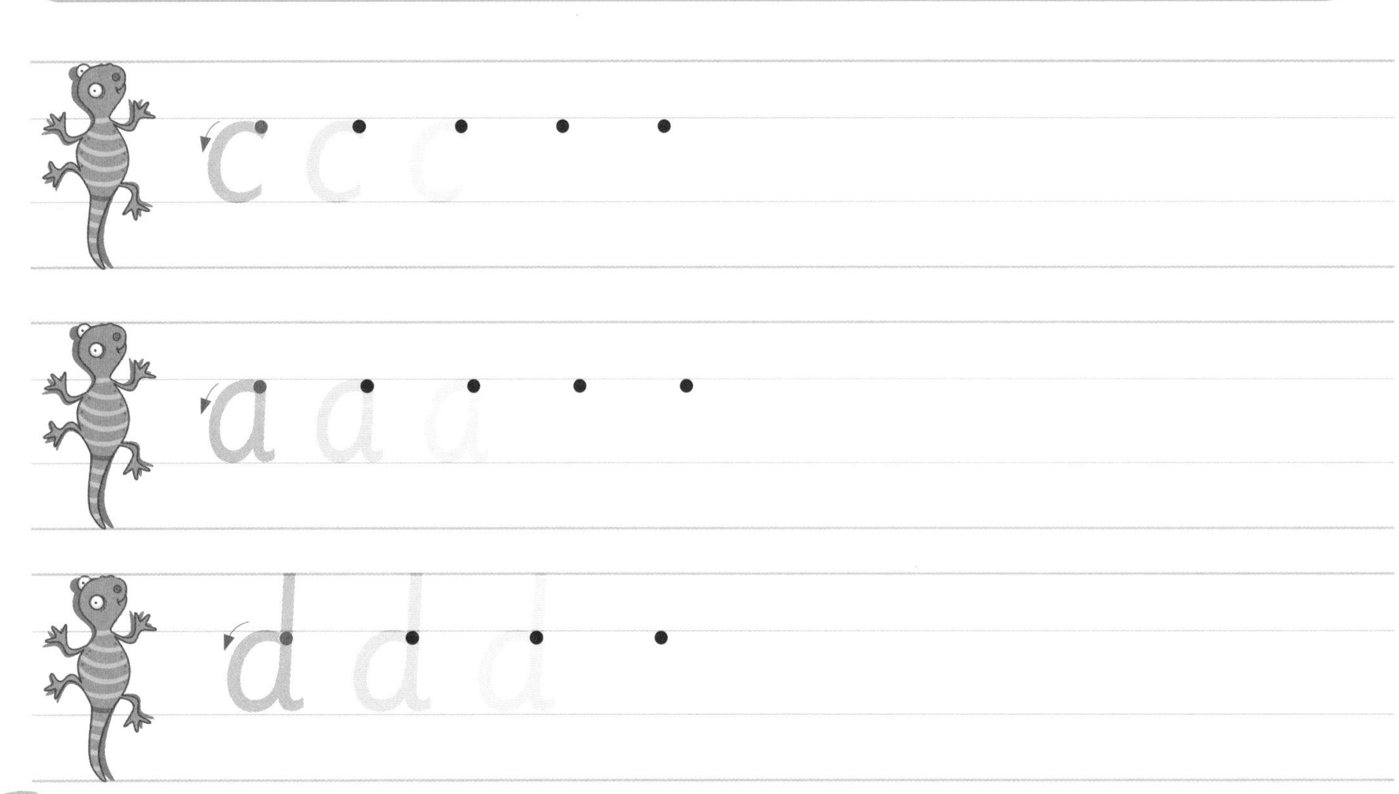

Trace over the curves.

g g

q q

o o

s s s

f f

e e

Notes: These nine letters are made using curves, loops and circles
f has curves at the top and the bottom, the line down is straight.

First zooming letter shapes

For some letters you need to know your zigzags, slants and crosses!

Draw the zigzags to complete the sky picture.

Trace over the letter and write some of your own.

Notes: These four letters are made using zig zags, slants and crosses. If you draw a square around **x** and **z**, each corner should touch the letter.

Straight down letters

Start at the top and go straight down.

Trace over the letter and write some of your own.

Practise

Straight down letters (2)

Start at the top and go straight down.

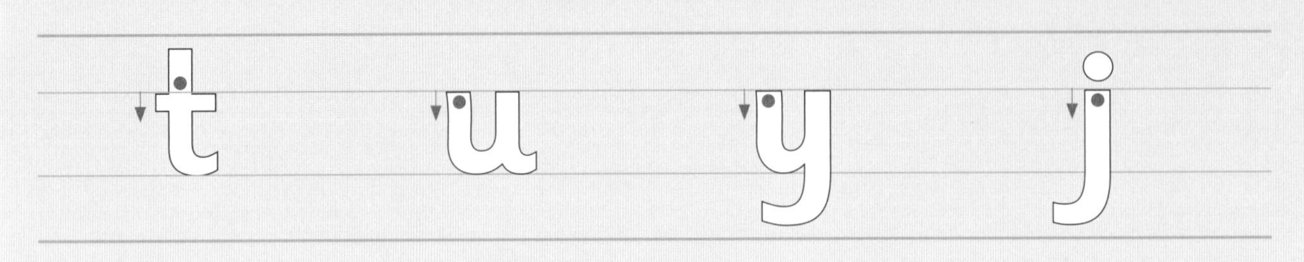

Trace over the letter and write some of your own.

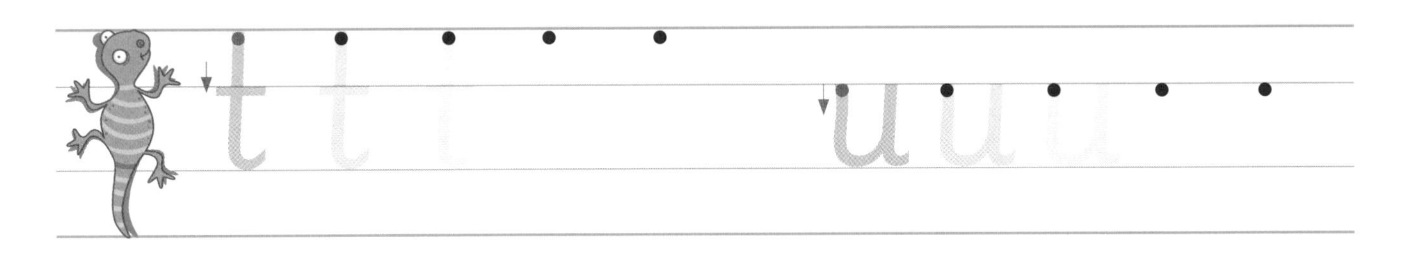

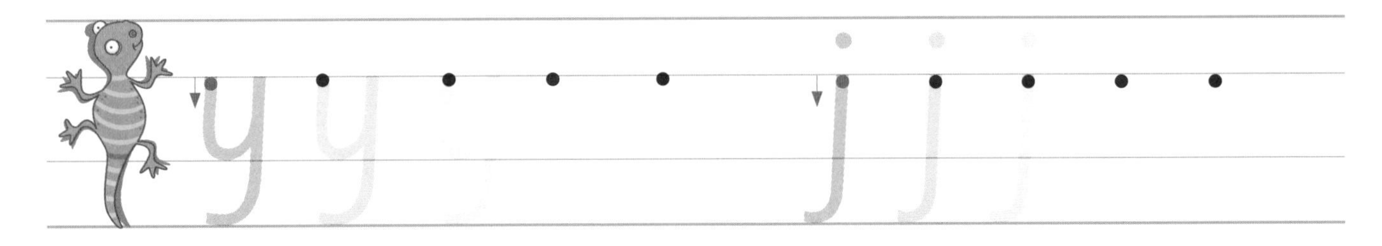

Practise

_ruck _et

Notes: Help your child to use straight lines that start from the top and go down to the writing line. The vertical lines in **u** and **y** must be parallel.

Down, up and over letters

Start at the top and go straight down, freeze, then straight back up and over.

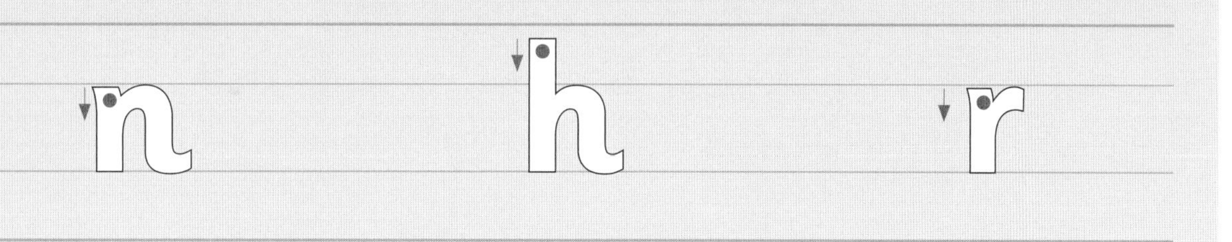

Trace over the letter and write some of your own.

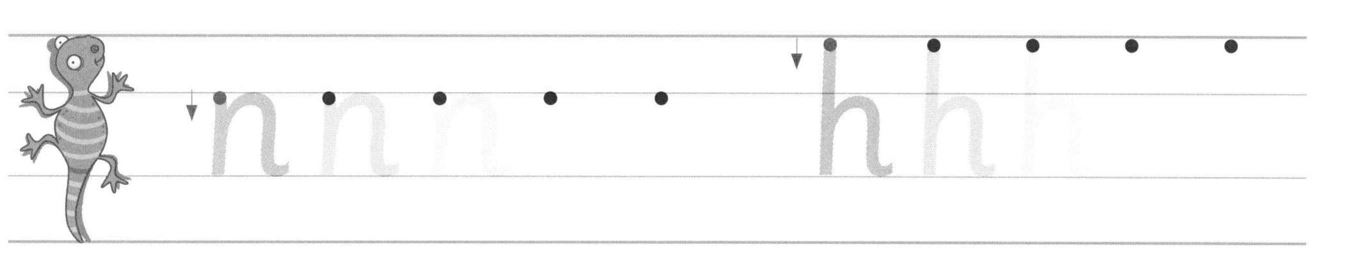

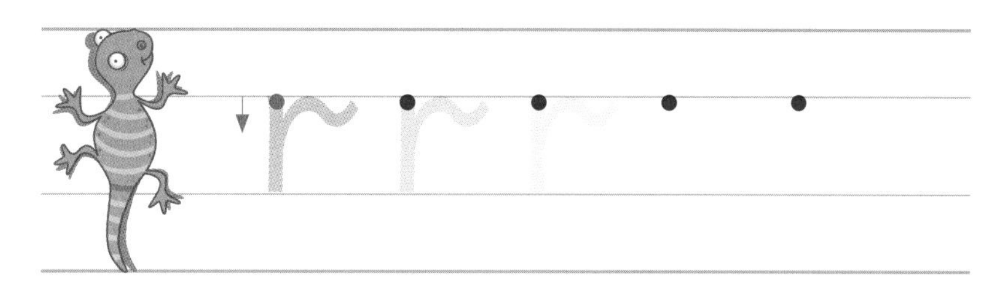

Practise

Notes: Remember to go straight down and freeze for a second, before drawing back up the stroke and over. The vertical lines in **h**, **n** and **m** must be parallel.

Down, up and over letters (2)

Start at the top and go straight down, freeze, then straight back up and over.

Trace over the letter and write some of your own.

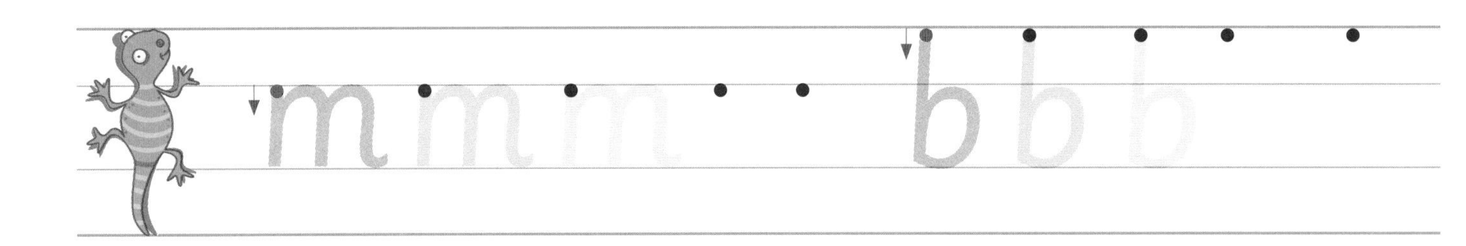

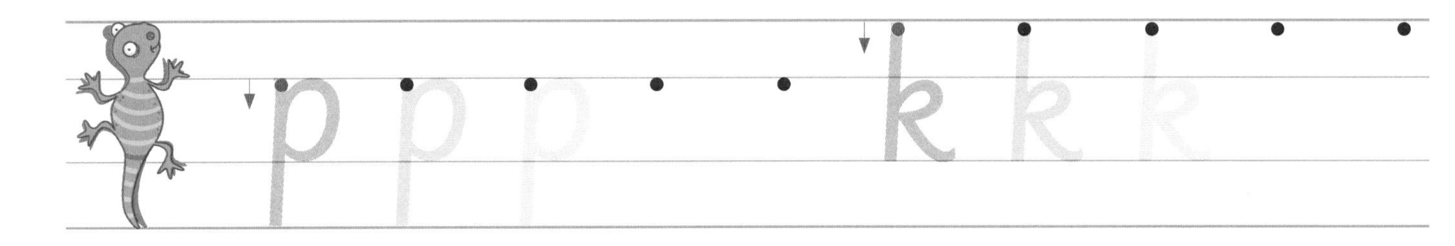

Practise

_ath

cloc_

Notes: Make sure both arches of the **m** are the same height and that the down line of the **p** remains straight. Do not go back too high with **k** and write a capital **R** by a mistake.

Up, backwards and around letters

Start at 1 o'clock. Go up, backwards and around.

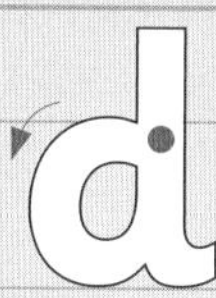

Trace over the letter and write some of your own.

c a

Practise

b_ll  _uck 

Notes: Help your child to identify the words and support them to form each letter – up, backwards and around from one o' clock.

Up, backwards and around letters (2)

Notes: Make your **o** completely round and finish right at the very top. Keep the downward vertical strokes of **g** and **q** straight.

Up, backwards and around letters (3)

Start at 1 o'clock. Go up, backwards and around.

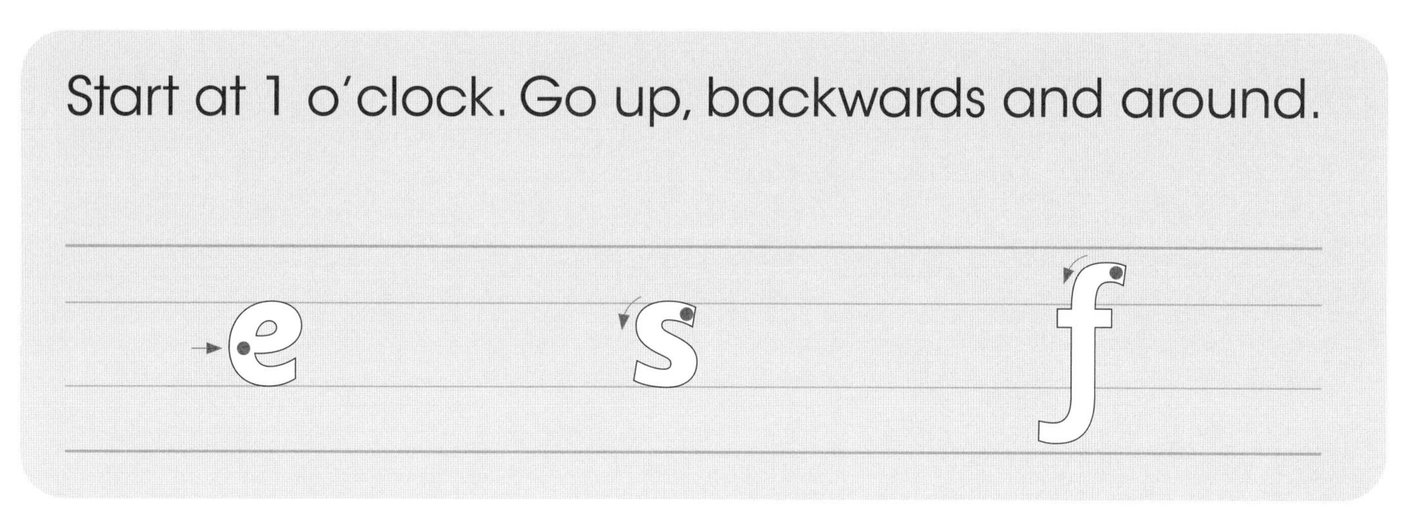

Practise

Notes: Make sure your child writes the **s** with equal half circles. Keep the downward vertical stroke of **f** straight.

Zooming letters

Left, diagonally down to the ground and back up right again.

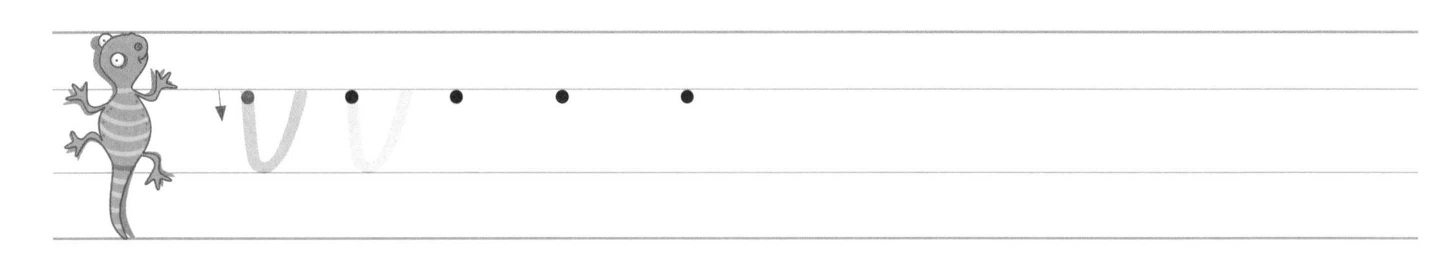

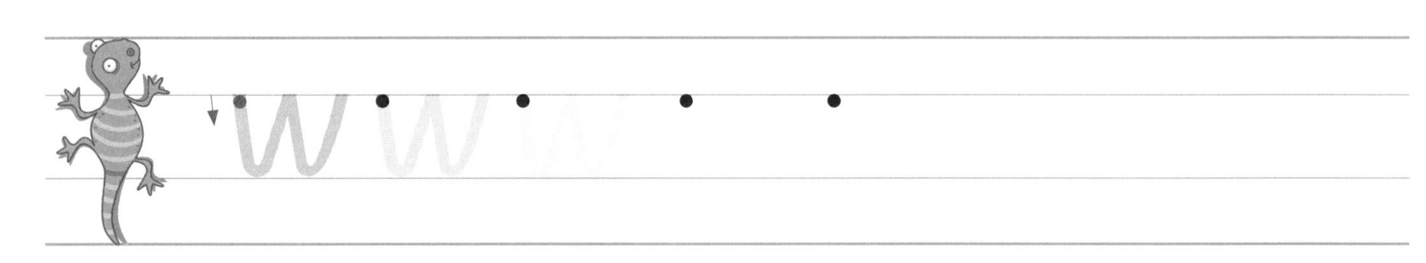

Practise

_an

glo_e

_atch

_a_e

Notes: Check each part of the **v** and **w** is the same size. Check the straight lines of **w** are slanted, not going vertically up and down.

Zooming letters (2)

Two more diagonal, slanted letters that sit on the ground.

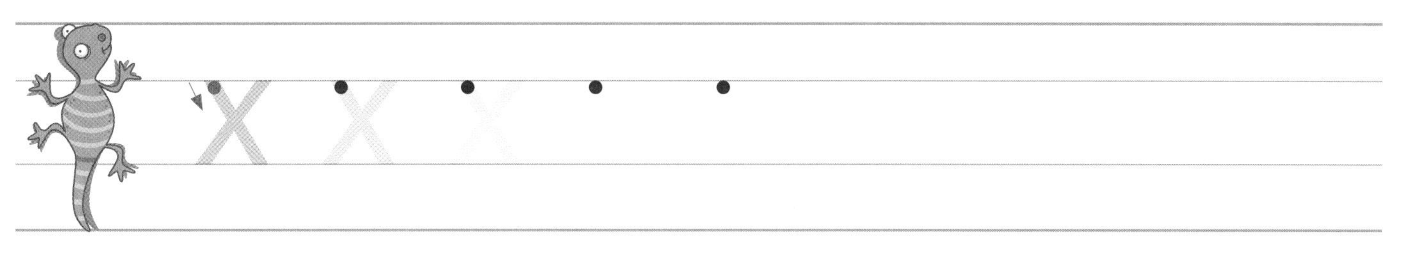

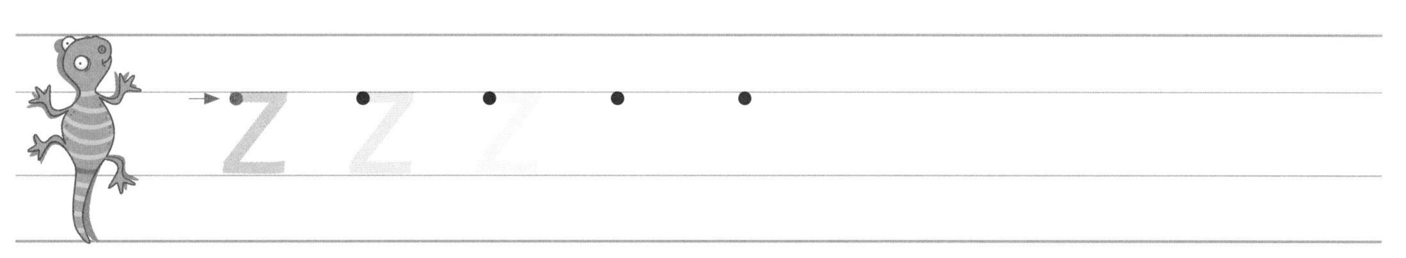

Practise

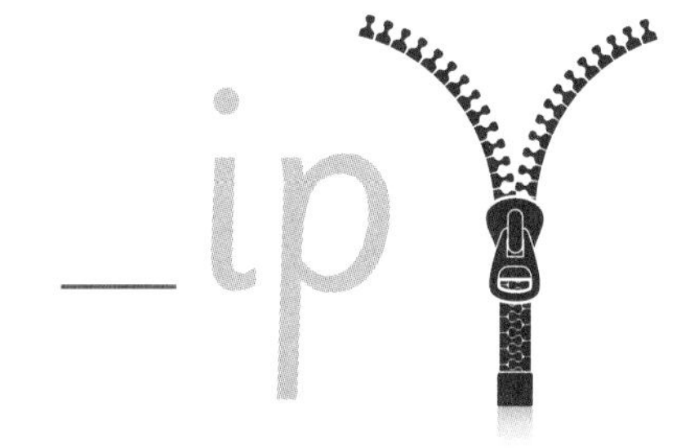

bu_ _

Notes: Take your pencil off the paper to form the **x**. Do not draw a **t**. Write the horizontals of the **z** along the top body and writing lines.

Straight down capitals

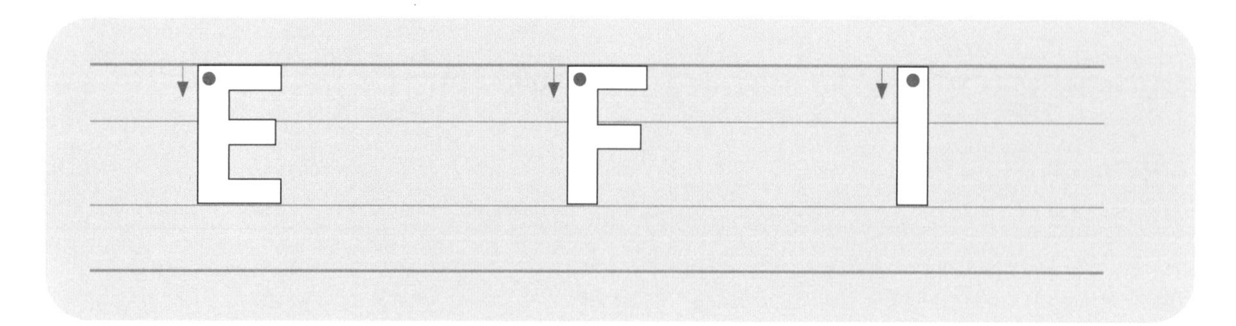

Trace over the capital letters. Write some of your own.

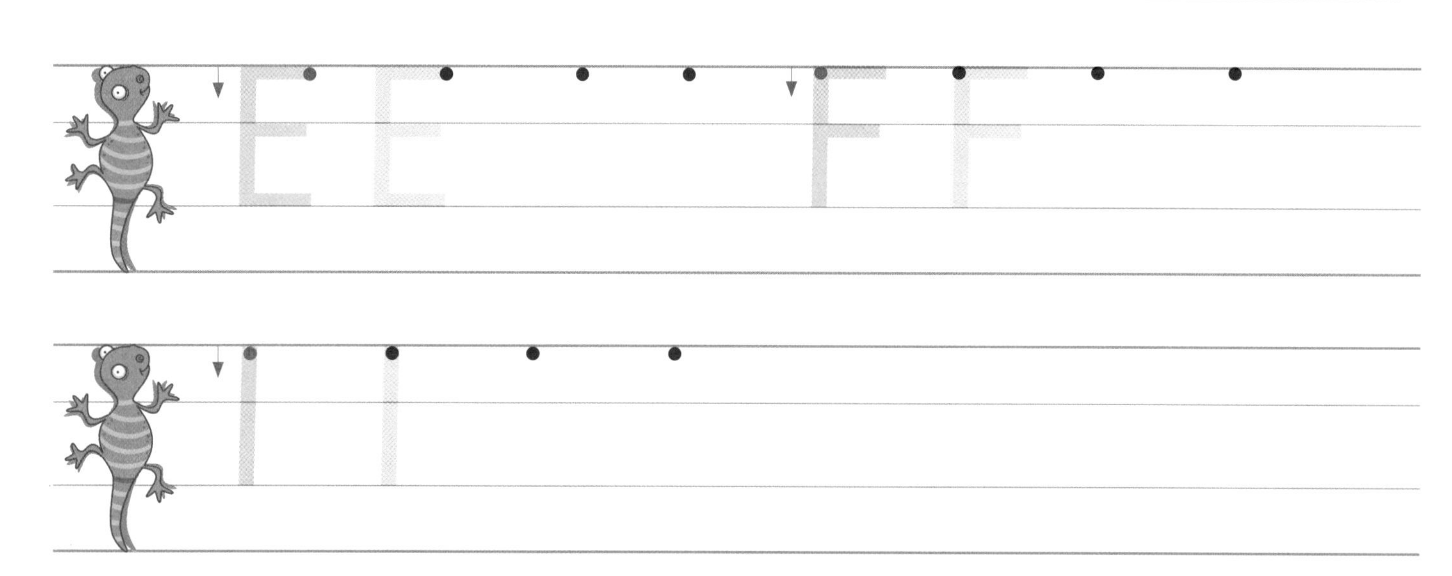

Trace the capital letters to complete the pictures.

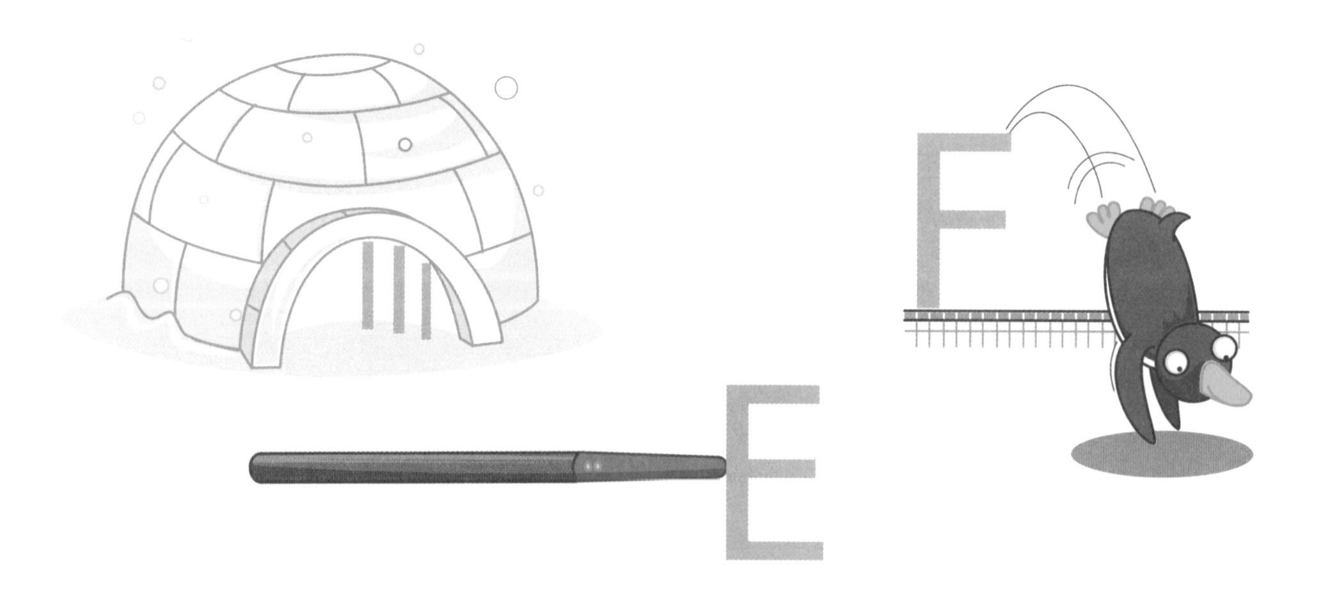

Notes: Check your child's horizontal lines on the **E** and **F** are straight. Let your child put a top and bottom horizontal line on the **I** if they want to.

Straight down capitals (2)

Trace over the capital letters. Write some of your own.

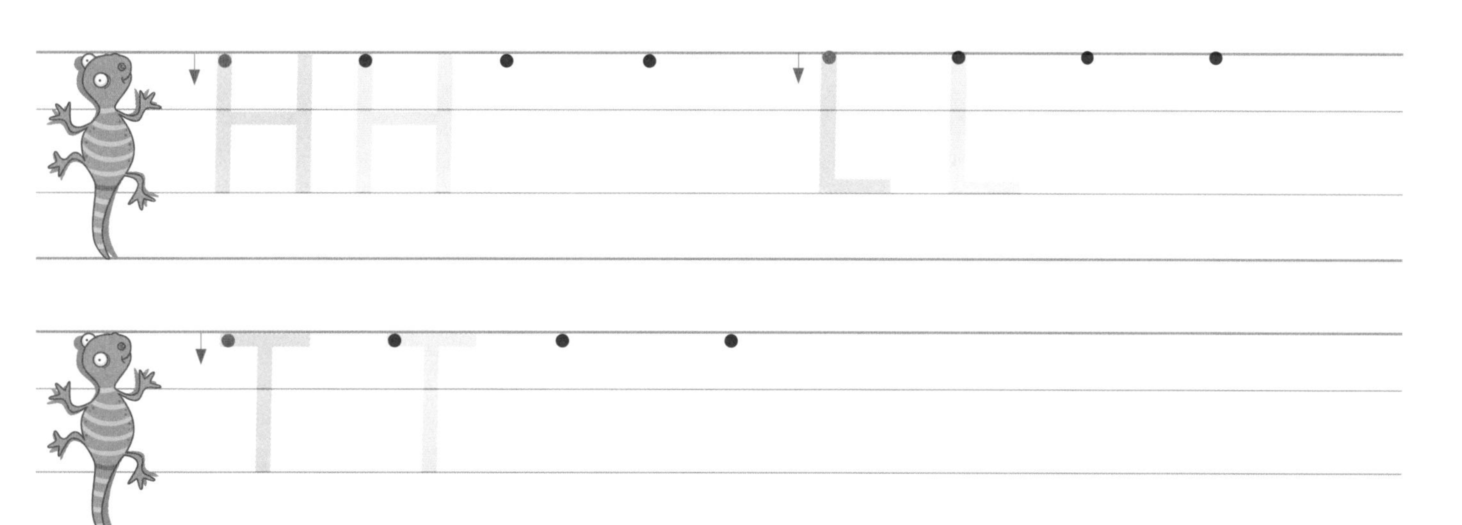

Trace the capital letters to complete the pictures.

Notes: Check the horizontal and vertical lines are straight and parallel on **H**, **L** and **T**.

Up, back and around capitals

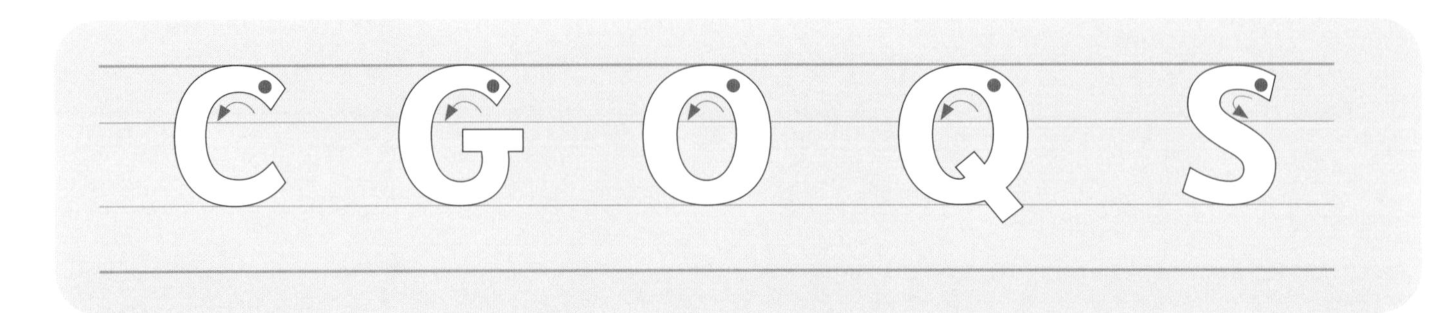

Trace over the capital letters. Write some of your own.

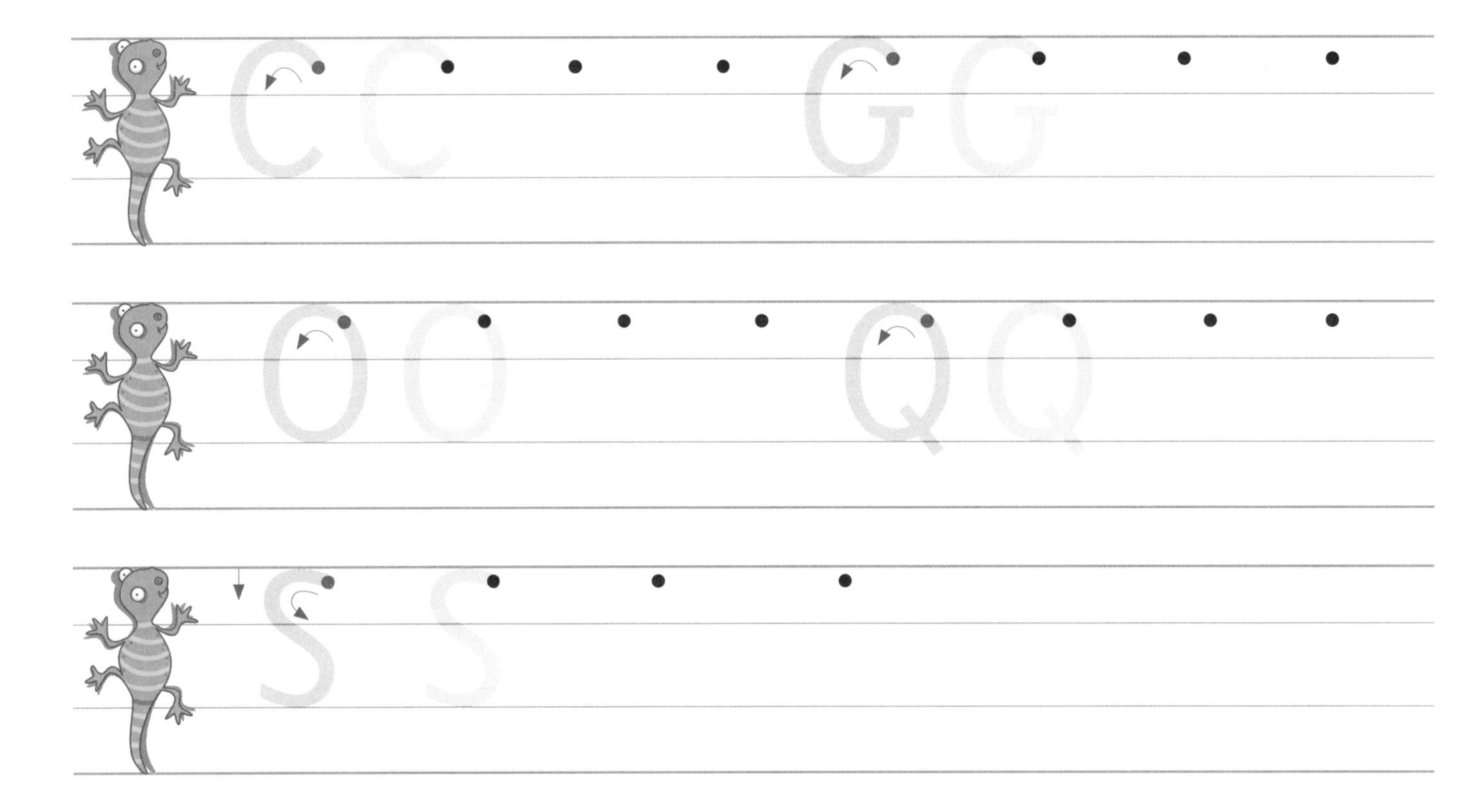

Trace the capital letters to complete the pictures.

Straight down and around capitals

Trace over the capital letters. Write some of your own.

Trace the capital letters to complete the pictures.

Slanted capitals

Trace over the capital letters. Write some of your own.

Trace the capital letters to complete the pictures.

Straight and slanted capitals

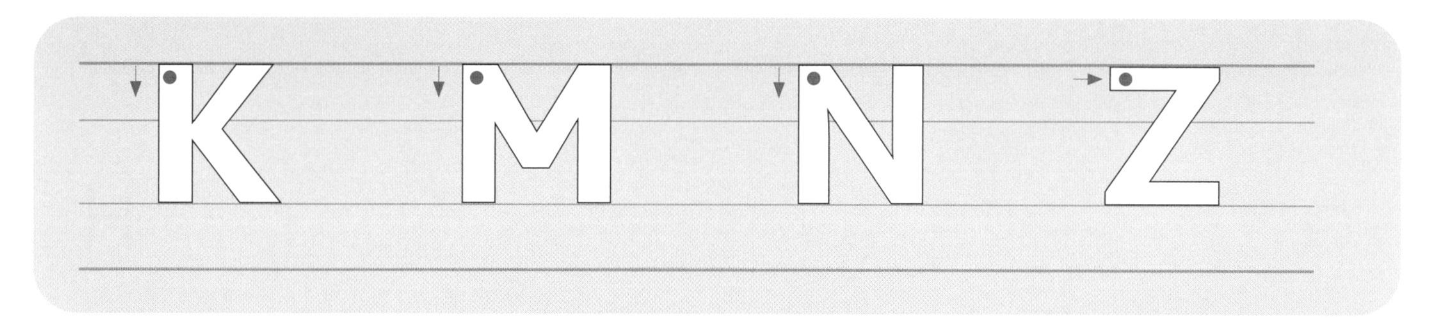

Trace over the capital letters. Write some of your own.

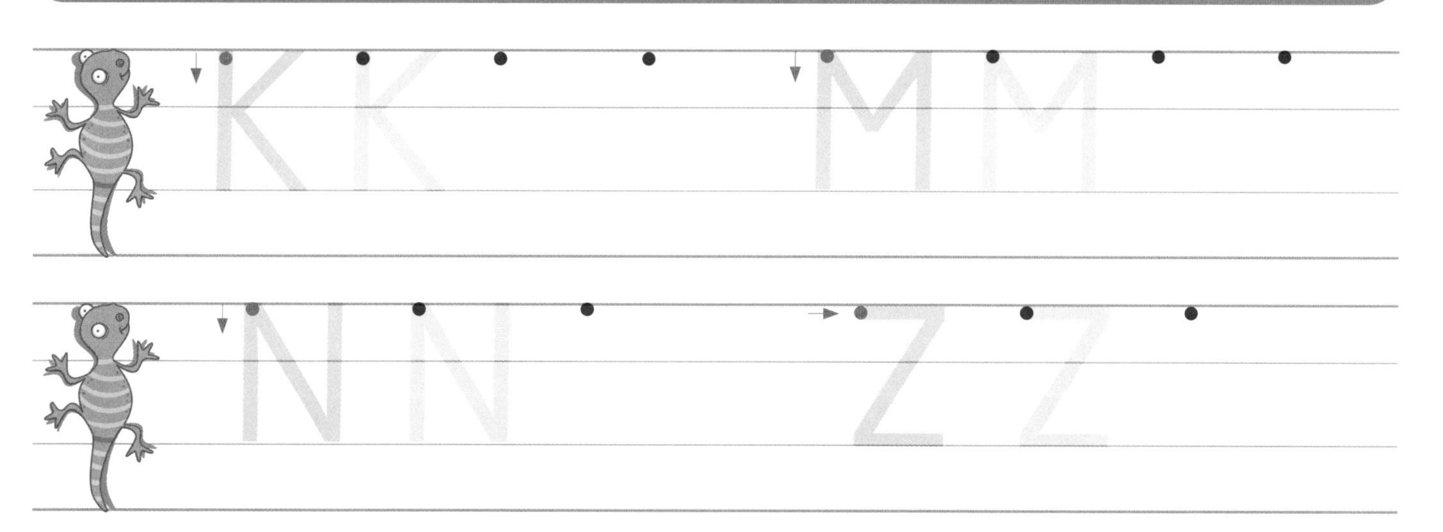

Trace the capital letters to complete the pictures.

Match the letters

Draw a line to match each lowercase letter to the capital letter.

a H

f A

b i G I

g B

d j E F

h D

e J

Write the capital letters for c, o, p and s.

Notes: Give your child plenty of practice of writing letters – play games such as hangman, write in steamy mirrors, make signs for your home (room names, drawer contents, object names).

Match the capital letters to the lowercase letters.

R q

M u

K T y m

N t

L U r l

Q k

Y n

Write the lowercase letters for V, W, X and Z.

Notes: When writing the lowercase letters, check both letter formation and sizing. The tram lines should help!

First Learning

Certificate

Well done!

You have completed

Early Writing

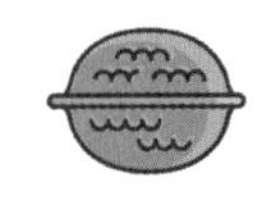

This certificate is awarded to:

....

Age: ....

Date: ....